The Outdoor Youth Adventures
Bow Hunting
Coloring Book

Top Brass Publishing
P.O. Box 209
Starkville, MS 39760
662-323-1559

Illustrated by Chris Armstrong
Concept by Steve Madar and Eric Cosby

Printed in the U.S.A. All Rights Reserved.

Copyright © 2005

www.OutdoorYouthAdventures.com

Code AAACBJJI

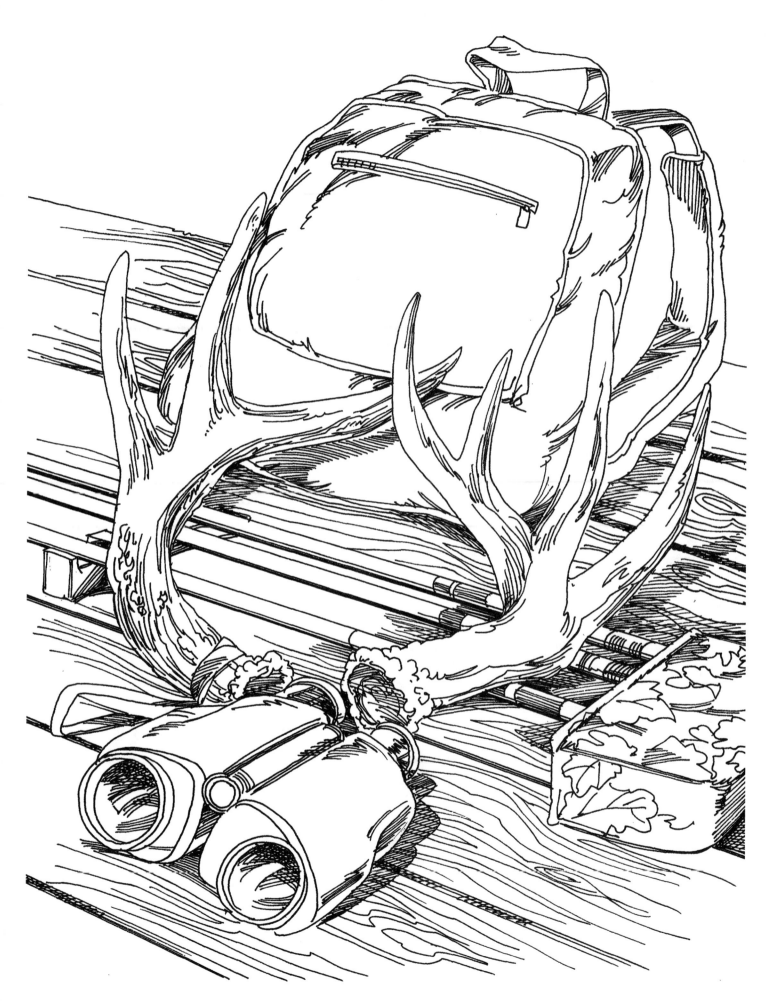

33

35